Growing up in Alaska
A Baby Arctic Tern

Constance Taylor

Illustrations: Ben the Illustrator

Photographs: Constance Taylor

Dedication
The Chugiak/Eagle River Senior Center Writing Group
and
the Arctic Tern family
who shared their 2017 summer activities
with a gaggle of photographers.

Library of Congress Control Number 2018945806
ISBN 978-1-888215-75-5 Hardcover
ISBN 978-1-888215-76-2 Paperback
ISBN ebook 978-1-888 215-76-9 e-book

Printed in the United States
Fathom Publishing Company
PO Box 200448
Anchorage, Alaska 99520
http://www.fathompublishing.com

Mom and Dad arrived in Alaska in May returning to the place they were born at Potter Marsh near Anchorage. They rested together after the 12,000 mile flight north from Antarctica.

Mom and Dad flew and fished together in the marsh. They rested and napped near each other when they were tired. They enjoyed taking baths and splashing in the clean waters.

Dad looked at Mom and said, "You are beautiful. I enjoy being with you. You can fly very fast and are able to catch lots of fish. Do you want to help me raise a chick this year?"

"Yes, I'd like to build a nest with you," said Mom.

So they built a nest together. First they found a safe spot on a small island in the marsh. Mom arranged the dried reeds and grass into a nest on the ground to make a safe place to lay my egg.

Mom and Dad took turns sitting on my egg keeping me warm while I grew. There was a yolk of food in my egg so I had everything I needed to develop into a baby Arctic Tern.

Soon I could hear Mom and Dad twittering and chirping to me. It was not long before I could peep back to them. I was eager to join them. I could tell their voices apart and I wanted to meet Mom and Dad.

I could tell my body was changing. I was starting to grow downy feathers all over. I thought to myself, "This must mean it's almost time to hatch. I wonder what the world is like."

I knew the big day had arrived. I started pecking at the inside of my shell. "Boy, this is hard work," I said to myself. I could hear Mom and Dad chirping encouragement.

When I finally scrambled out from the shell, my down was damp. Mom held me under her wing while I dried out and got used to the new feelings of being free from my shell. I could stand on my own two legs for the first time.

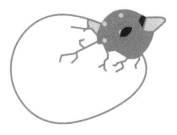

Suddenly I felt a strange feeling inside my belly.

"What's happening," I cheeped to Mom, "I never felt this way before."

I was scared.

Dad showed up with a dragonfly and dropped it in my beak.

Mom explained, "Now that you're hatched, you have to eat bugs and fish to keep from being hungry. Your yolk is all used up and you left it behind when you hatched."

Now I understood the strange way I felt.

"Where's Mom going?" I asked Dad.

"She's gone to find more bugs for you." Dad told me they would take turns bringing me bugs and fish until I was big enough to catch my own food.

"Don't worry," he said, "one of us will stay near you all the time until you are grown up."

When I watched Mom fly away, I felt a new urge. I wanted to fly too. I stretched out my wings.

"That's right," said Dad. "It feels good to stretch your wings. Your feathers are starting to grow. In a few weeks, they will be longer and your bones will be stronger. You will be able to fly just like Mom."

"Dad, why do I look different? You and Mom are white and gray. You have a black cap on your head."

"Your baby down is a special mixture of colors that blend in with the color of the rocks and grasses," Dad explained. "When both Mom and I are away, it is important for you to crouch down and hide. We don't want anyone to see you while we are gone."

I showed Dad how I could hide in the grass. "I'll be careful," I said.

"When you grow up, you will grow new feathers with colors just like us," said Dad.

I started getting interested in the world around me. When it was warm and sunny, I wandered around in the grass. I was happy as long as I could return to the nest and get under Mom or Dad's wing when it rained.

One day I was adventurous and wandered farther from the nest than ever before. I found water for the first time.

"Don't be afraid," Mom told me. "You can swim."

"Yes, I really can," I said as I waded into the water. I could float. I paddled my feet and learned to swim. This was really fun.

I swam farther away from our nest until I found a perfect rock.

Mom and Dad called to me. "Come back to our island. We want you to stay close to the nest so we can take care of you."

"No, I am a big bird now," I said. "I'm ready to meet the world."

So they started to bring fish and dragonflies to my rock.

My rock was almost the same colors as my down and feathers.
I could sleep in the sun and feel safe and comfortable.

I always felt safest when Mom and Dad were close by. Sometimes both Mom and Dad would nap together on the tall rock next to me where I could look up and see them.

Mom and Dad kept a close eye on the other birds and animals in Potter Marsh. They always protected me. One day Dad chased a Canada Goose away from my rock.

There were lots of things to learn as my feathers started to grow.

"You need to preen many times a day to keep your feathers clean and neatly arranged," Mom said. "You won't be able to stay warm or even fly if you don't take care of your feathers."

Sometimes Mom and Dad would land on my rock next to me and give me a bug.

Other times they would just fly by my rock and drop small fish into my beak while hovering over me.

When I hatched out of my egg, my wings were tiny. Now they were growing longer and longer. I was getting more feathers every day.

"Look, Dad," I said, "my wings are longer than my whole body now."

Dad told me, "Practice flapping your wings to build up their strength. One day you will be surprised when you lift yourself into the air."

Mom encouraged me by walking just ahead of me. I ran along flapping my wings just as hard as I could.

I watched how Mom and Dad would stretch out their wings and leap into the air. I wanted to be able to fly with them.

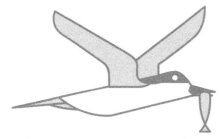

Mom and Dad called to me as they were flying back with food. I would stand tall on my rock and cheep as loudly as I could. I'd be ready to eat whatever they had to drop into my beak.

Fish were my favorite food. As I grew bigger, I was able to eat bigger fish. Sometimes they were so big I had to struggle to swallow them. Some of the fish had large spines that made them even harder to eat.

Swallow fish head first," Mom said.

Even Mom and Dad had trouble swallowing the fish with spines.

As I got older, I learned more about taking care of my feathers. I liked washing in the pond. I would wade into the water and then toss and splash to get every feather wet. I even put my head under the water.

I would carefully preen my feathers so they were all straight and neatly arranged. Then I poked my beak under my wing and took a nap in the sun. My life was perfect.

I was learning lots of new things but most of all I wanted to learn to fly like Mom and Dad. I faced into the wind like Dad showed me. Then I tried to fly from my rock by jumping into the air and stretching my wings. I only stayed in the air for a second and then I landed in the water. I had to swim back to my rock.

When I looked at myself in the water, I could see my baby down was falling out. New black feathers were growing on my head. I was going to look like Mom and Dad with a sleek black cap. I could tell I was really growing up and would soon be able to fly.

I practiced and practiced and one day I did lift off into the air just like Dad said would happen.

"Wow!" I cried out. "This is the most fun I've ever had in my whole life."

Learn more about Arctic Terns

Read about Arctic Terns at The CornellLab of Ornithology: https://www.allaboutbirds.org/guide/Arctic_Tern/lifehistory

See where in the world Arctic Terns have been observed at iNaturalist: https://www.inaturalist.org/taxa/4449-Sterna-paradisaea

Watch videos of this Arctic Tern growing up at Fathom Twist: http://www.fathomtwist.com/birds/arctictern

Make an online visit to the Yakatat Arctic Tern Festival: http://www.yakutatternfestival.org

Arctic Terns avoid the winter by spending summers in Alaska and migrating to the southern tip of South America and Antarctica during the northern winter months. The line shows the Pacific migration route. Arctic Terns have the longest migration of any animal.